Things to make and do with Paper

Amanda Gulliver
and Stephanie Turnbull

Illustrations by Molly Sage
Cover design by Nicola Butler
Photographs by Howard Allman

Contents

There are lots of stickers in the middle of this book.
You can use them to decorate the things you make.

Fairytale castle

1. Tear a long strip of green paper for the grass. Glue it to the bottom of a big sheet of paper.

Make the rectangles different sizes.

2. Rip some rectangles from bright paper. You could use giftwrap or pages from a magazine.

3. Glue the biggest shape in the middle. Add other rectangles at the sides, overlapping each other.

4. Cut out some triangles for the turrets. Make sure they are bigger than the tops of the rectangles.

5. Glue the turrets on top of the rectangles. Cut out a door and glue it onto the castle.

6. Cut out window shapes from darker paper and glue them on. Add some window sills.

7. To make trees, rip bright circles of paper and tear strips for trunks. Glue them onto the grass.

Use different shades and textures of paper to make your castle look really magical.

3

Paper gliders

You could decorate a glider with stickers or bright patterns.

 You can use writing paper, giftwrap or an old magazine.

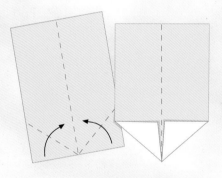

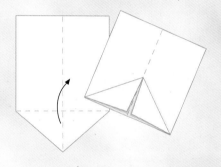

1. Cut out a rectangle of bright paper. Fold the long edges together and unfold them again.

2. Now fold the bottom corners in. Make sure the bottom edges meet the middle crease.

3. Turn the paper over. Fold up the bottom point as shown above and crease the fold well.

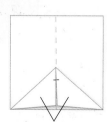

Triangular flaps

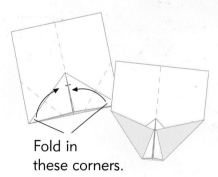

Fold in these corners.

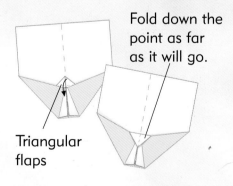

Fold down the point as far as it will go.

Triangular flaps

4. Mark a point about a third of the way down the triangular flaps, as shown above.

5. Fold in the bottom corners so that they meet at this point. Crease the folds well.

6. Fold the top point of the triangular flaps down over the triangles you made in step 5.

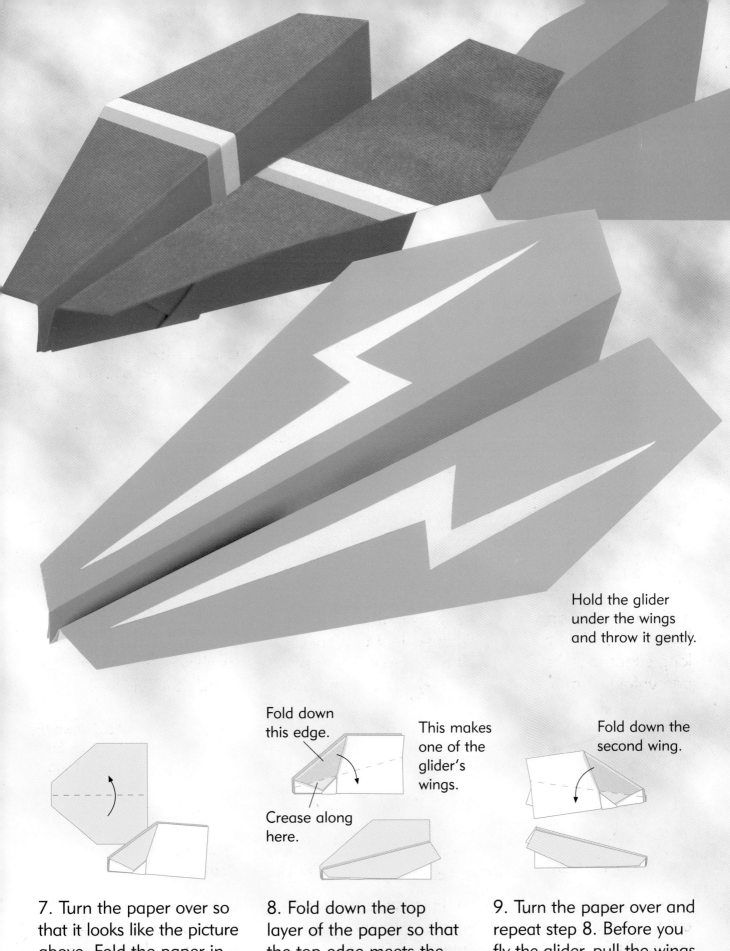

Hold the glider
under the wings
and throw it gently.

Fold down
this edge.

This makes
one of the
glider's
wings.

Crease along
here.

Fold down the
second wing.

7. Turn the paper over so that it looks like the picture above. Fold the paper in half from bottom to top.

8. Fold down the top layer of the paper so that the top edge meets the bottom edge of the paper.

9. Turn the paper over and repeat step 8. Before you fly the glider, pull the wings out to the sides a little.

Bird mask

Fold

1. Fold some stiff paper in half. Lay some sunglasses along the bottom, halfway across the fold.

2. Draw around the shape and open out the paper. Add an eye, then make a hole in it with a pencil.

3. Push scissors into the hole. Cut to the edge of the eye, then cut it out. Fold the paper again.

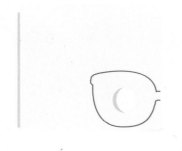

4. Draw around the eye shape onto the paper below and cut it out. Fold the paper again.

Edge of mask

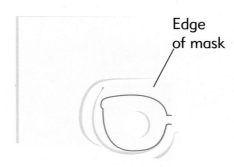

5. Draw a curved line around the shape for the edge of your mask. Cut through both layers.

6. Cut a 10cm (4in.) square of bright paper for the beak. Fold the corners together.

7. Draw a line from the middle of one short side to the other corner. Cut along the line.

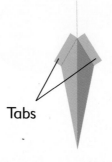

Tabs

8. Make a small snip along the top of the fold. Bend the sides to make tabs. Glue them to the mask.

9. Cut feather shapes from giftwrap, crêpe paper or tissue paper. Make them about as long as a finger.

6

You could use zigzag scissors or pinking shears to cut out the eye circles.

Don't glue feather shapes over the eye holes.

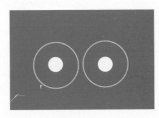

10. Glue the feather shapes around the edge of the mask, then glue on more and overlap them.

11. Lay the mask on some paper and draw around the eye holes. Cut them out. Draw circles around them.

12. Cut out the circles and glue them onto the mask. Tape some elastic to the mask to wear it.

Patterned paper houses

1. Cut a zigzag at one end of a strip of cardboard. Then, paint a rectangle of acrylic paint on a piece of thick paper.

2. Drag the zigzag end of the cardboard across the paint again and again to make textured lines. Leave the paint to dry.

3. Cut several small triangles into the end of another strip of cardboard. Drag it across another rectangle of paint.

Make lots of different
striped and checked
houses to create a
street of bright buildings.

4. Make some more
textured patches of paint
by experimenting with
different shapes cut into
strips of cardboard.

5. Cut rectangles from the
painted paper for houses,
windows, doors and roofs.
Glue them onto a big
piece of cardboard.

Dolly paperchain

1. Take two pieces of plain paper and tape them together, as shown.

2. Fold the paper in half. Then, fold it again so that you get a zigzag shape.

3. Draw the dolly's head near the top of the paper. Then, add her dress.

You can join your dollies into one long chain and hang them up.

4. Draw the dolly's arms all the way to the edge of the paper. Add her hair.

5. Draw legs to the edge of the paper. Then, go over the shape with a pen.

6. Cut out the dolly shape, along the pen lines. Don't cut along the folds.

Draw a face on each dolly.

7. Open out the shape and turn it over. Decorate the dollies with tissue paper.

11

Tissue paper flowers

Fold the paper with
the tape on the inside.

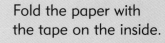

1. Cut a strip of tissue
paper as long as this book
and half as wide. Fold it in
half, long sides together.

2. Open out the paper.
Carefully stick a long piece
of tape along the fold.
Fold the paper again.

3. Fold the paper in
half, with the short sides
together. Then, fold it in
half again.

Folded
edge

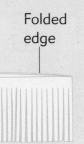

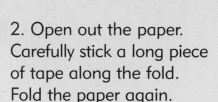

4. Make lots of cuts from
the bottom edge (not from
the folded edge). Don't
cut all the way to the top.

5. Open out the paper
very carefully. Then, lay
it flat, with the cut edge
at the top.

6. Tape the folded edge
to the end of a straw
and start to roll the paper
tightly around the straw.

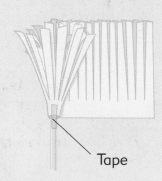

Tape

7. Secure the paper
with more tape every
now and then. This will
keep it tightly rolled.

8. When all the paper is
rolled up, tape down the
end. Pull down the cut
ends to make petals.

9. Roll some orange
tissue paper into a ball.
Glue it to the middle of
the flower.

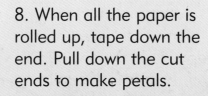

Cut some leaves out
of green paper.

Make a big
bunch of flowers
using lots of
different shades
of tissue paper.

To make a poppy

Glue a ball
of tissue
paper in
the middle.

1. Lay two sheets of
tissue paper together. Put
a saucer on top of them
and draw around it.

2. Cut around the circle
through both layers of
paper. Fold the circle in
half, then in half again.

3. Twist the corner and
tape it onto the end of
a straw. Pull the petals
apart, gently.

Cut-out clowns

1. For the body, cut a large triangle from bright paper. Cut two smaller triangles for arms and glue them on the back.

2. Cut a circle for the clown's head and glue it to the top of the body. Cut a hat shape and glue it onto the head.

3. For the clown's hair, cut out funny shapes from bright paper. Glue them onto the sides of the clown's head.

4. Cut out hands and legs and glue them on. Remember to glue them to the back of the clown.

5. To make striped socks, cut little strips of paper and glue them onto the legs. Glue on two big clown shoe shapes.

6. Use felt-tip pens to draw the clown's face. You could also tape some thread onto the hat for hanging up your clown.

You can make all
kinds of hat shapes
for your clowns.

Hang your clown
in a window or
glue it to a card.

You could decorate
a clown's outfit
with lots of bright
stickers.

15

Lacy cards

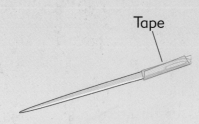
Tape

1. Draw shapes on thick paper. Put the paper on top of a pile of old magazines.

2. Wrap tape around the blunt end of a thick needle to make a handle.

3. Use the needle to prick around the shapes. Press hard.

4. Cut around the shapes carefully. Leave a narrow edge around the holes.

5. Dab glue on the pencil side of each shape. Press them onto thin cardboard.

6. To make a card, glue your picture onto a bigger piece of folded cardboard.

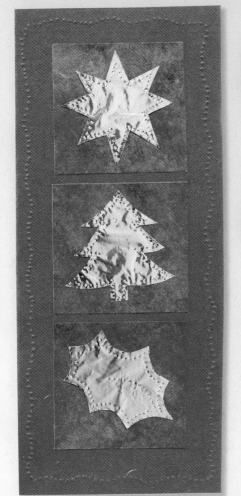

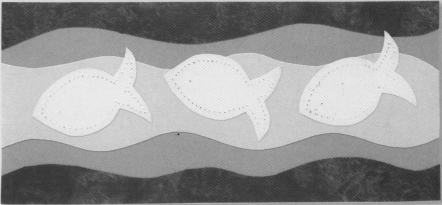

You could cut shapes from kitchen foil to make a Christmas card.

Make waves from blue paper for a fish or boat card.

Shiny necklace

Roll the giftwrap tightly.

1. Cut a piece of shiny giftwrap as long as a drinking straw and as tall as your little finger.

2. Cover the back of the giftwrap with glue. Lay the straw along one edge and roll it up in the paper.

3. Cover more straws with shiny giftwrap. For a very long necklace you will need five straws.

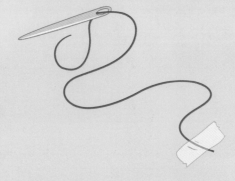

4. When the glue is dry, cut the straws into different sizes of beads. Cut some long and some short.

5. Thread a blunt needle with strong thread. Tape the end of the thread to a work surface.

6. Thread on the beads until you have used them all. Tie the ends to make a necklace.

Make sure the necklace is long enough to go over your head.

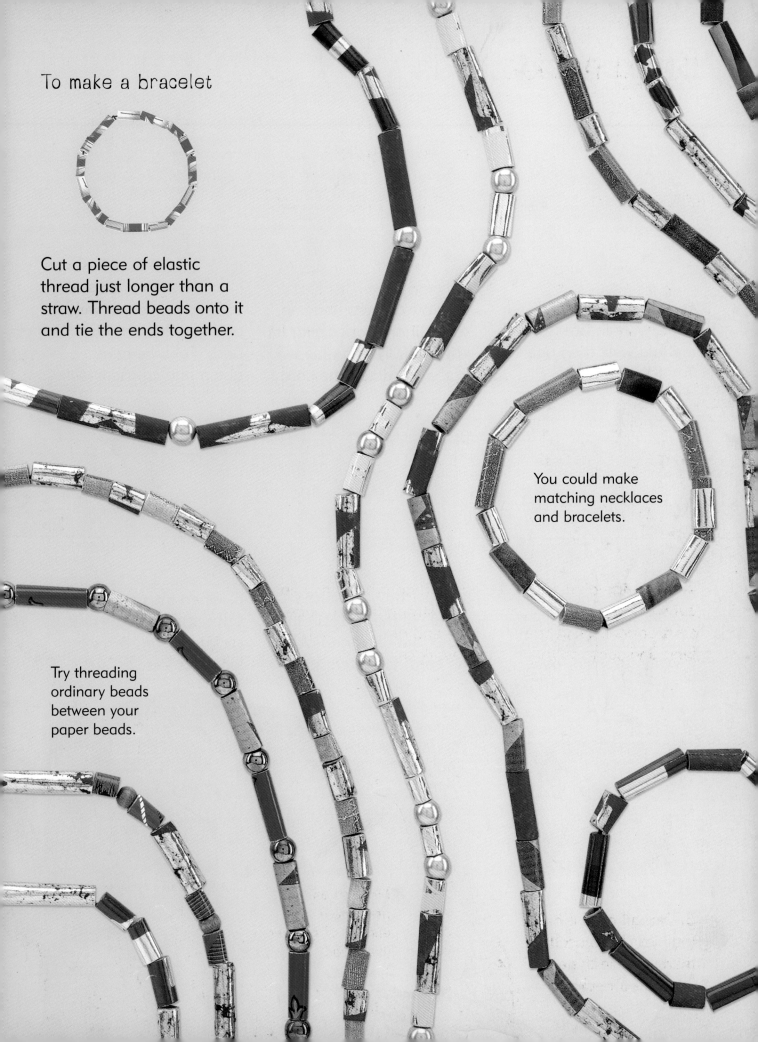

To make a bracelet

Cut a piece of elastic
thread just longer than a
straw. Thread beads onto it
and tie the ends together.

You could make
matching necklaces
and bracelets.

Try threading
ordinary beads
between your
paper beads.

Beaky bird cards

1. Fold a piece of stiff paper in half. Crease the fold well, then open it out again.

2. Draw a bird's body on some bright paper. Tear it out carefully and glue it to the middle of the card.

3. Tear out some wings and glue them to the body. Fold the card again and crease it well.

Crayon the inside, too.

4. Cut the corner off an old envelope to make the beak. You can brighten it with crayons or pens.

5. Glue the beak in the middle of the fold. Lift the top of the beak and close the card, to flatten it.

6. Open the card again. Cut out some eyes and stick them on. Draw in legs and feet.

Add different shapes to make the background look interesting.

7. Draw flowers around the bird, or cut them out from bright paper and glue them on.

20

To make a long card, glue body shapes over the fold, then add the beaks.

Fairy pictures

Keep this quarter for later.

Remove these parts.

1. Put a small plate onto a sheet of paper and draw around it with a pencil. Cut out the circle you have drawn.

2. Fold the circle in half, then in half again, and open it out. Then, cut along two of the folds and remove one quarter.

3. Draw two wing shapes touching the folds. Cut around the shapes and along the folds to make the wings, as shown.

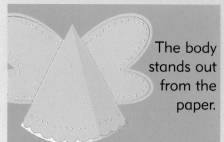

The body stands out from the paper.

4. Decorate the body and wings. Push the wings together, so the body curves, and glue them to another circle of paper.

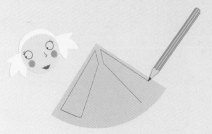

5. Cut out a head and draw a face. Then, cut out hair and glue it on. Draw two arms on the paper quarter you kept earlier.

Decorate the picture with shiny stickers.

You could put a fairy picture on your bedroom door.

Decorate the arms.

6. Cut out the arms. Then, cut out hands and glue them onto the arms. Glue the arms and the head onto the body.

7. For legs, cut two long strips of paper. Make one end of each leg rounded, then fold the legs lots of times, to make zigzags.

8. Glue the legs under the body, so they dangle down. Make sure that the rounded ends are at the bottom.

Jumping frogs

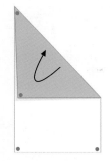

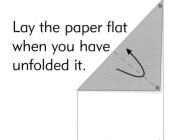

Lay the paper flat when you have unfolded it.

1. Cut some paper about 8 x 13cm (3 x 5in.). Mark the corners on both sides in red and blue, as shown.

2. Lay the paper flat and fold one blue corner across to the opposite edge. Unfold it again.

3. Fold the other blue corner across to the opposite side in the same way and unfold it.

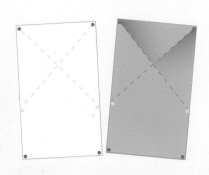

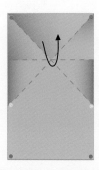

This is the last crease.

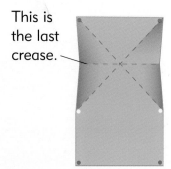

4. Mark the ends of the new creases (made in steps 2 and 3) in yellow on both sides of the paper.

5. Turn the paper over and fold the edge with blue corners down to the yellow marks. Now unfold it.

6. Put a finger at each end of the last crease and push gently inward. The middle should pop up.

Point

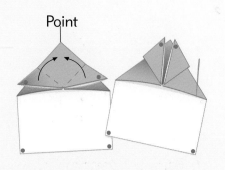

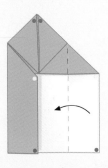

7. Flatten the blue corners down behind, so that they touch the yellow marks.

8. Turn the paper over and fold the blue corners up to the point. This makes the front feet.

9. Fold the left and right sides in so that they meet in the middle. Crease the folds well.

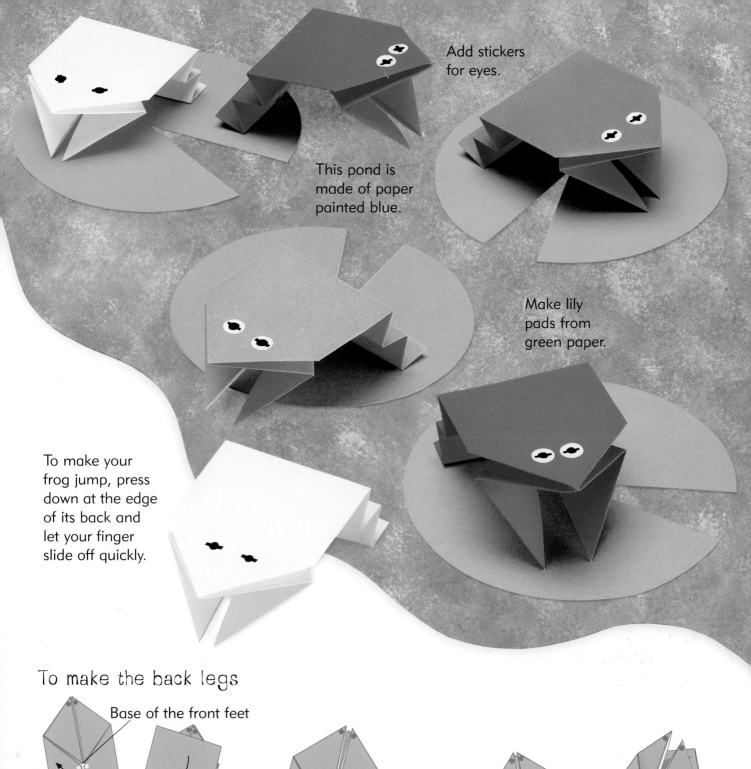

Add stickers for eyes.

This pond is made of paper painted blue.

Make lily pads from green paper.

To make your frog jump, press down at the edge of its back and let your finger slide off quickly.

To make the back legs

Base of the front feet

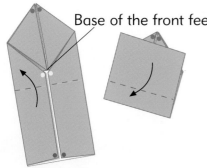

Crease it at this edge.

1. Fold up 4cm (1.5in.) of the bottom edge. Then, fold the paper back down and crease it at the base of the front feet.

2. Fold the bottom edge up again and crease it at the bottom edge of the paper underneath, as shown above.

3. Finally, bring the top edge back to meet all the bottom folds. Pull the front legs out so that your frog can stand.

Tissue paper butterflies

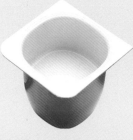

1. Pour household glue (PVA) into a container. Mix in a few drops of water.

2. Cut a long, oval shape from tissue paper for the body of your butterfly.

Use a paintbrush to glue the tissue to the paper.

3. Cut a circle for the head. Glue the head and body onto a piece of paper.

4. Tear two different shades of tissue paper into large wing shapes.

5. Glue the wings onto the paper, crumpling and overlapping them.

6. Cut or rip some smaller shapes. Glue them onto the wings as decoration.

7. Use a brush to paint glue all over your butterfly. This makes it shiny.

8. When the glue is dry, use a thin felt-tip pen to add details.

Pop-up cards

Make sure both cuts
are the same length.

1. Cut two pieces of paper the same size. Fold one of them in half, so that the short edges are together.

2. Make two small cuts in the middle of the folded edge. Fold back the flap between the cuts.

3. Now fold the flap over the other way and crease it. Unfold the flap, then open the card.

You could make pop-up Christmas or birthday cards.

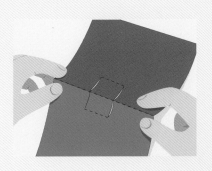 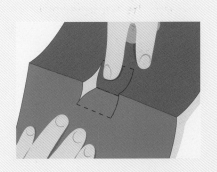

4. Pinch along the fold on either side of the flap. Hold the paper at each end of the fold, not near the flap.

5. Push the flap down with your finger. Close the card carefully and smooth it flat. Open the card.

6. Fold the other piece of paper in half. Glue the two pieces together, with the middle folds together.

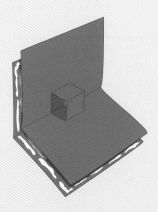

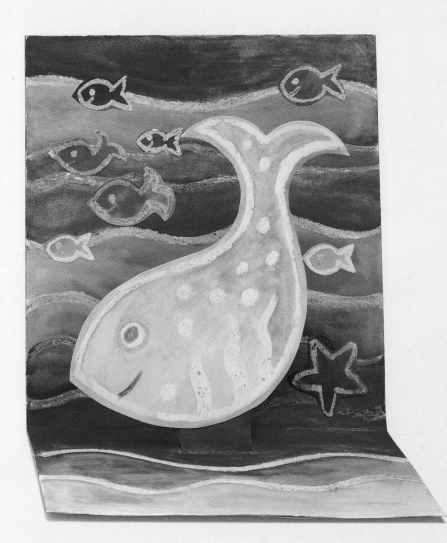

7. Draw a picture on a piece of paper the same size as your folded card. Cut it out.

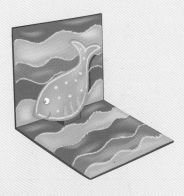

8. Use felt-tip pens to decorate the inside of the card. Glue your picture onto the front of the flap.

Flower gift tags

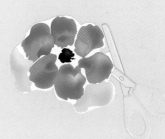

1. Wet a sheet of paper thoroughly, then shake off any drips. Lay it flat on a waterproof surface.

2. Dab on blobs of paint to make petals. The paint will smudge and spread across the wet paper.

3. Add a contrasting blob to each petal, a black blob in the middle and green blobs for leaves.

4. Leave the sheet of paper to dry. Don't move the paper before it is dry, or the paint will run.

5. Roughly cut around the flowers, then glue them onto thin cardboard. Leave the glue to dry.

6. Cut out the flowers, leaving a thin border around the edges. Cut off any extra smudges.

Write a message on the back of a tag and attach it to your present.

You could also
glue flowers
onto plain
giftwrap to
decorate it.

Picture frames

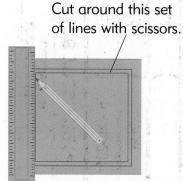

Cut around this set of lines with scissors.

1. Cut out two pieces of thin cardboard, bigger than the picture you're framing.

2. Lay your picture on one of the pieces of cardboard. Draw around it in pencil.

3. Draw another set of lines inside the first lines. Cut around the inner shape.

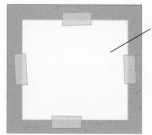

Tape the picture face down, like this.

You could decorate your frame before you tape the picture to it.

4. Tape your picture to the frame. Glue the other piece of cardboard on the back.

The frame on the right has small pieces of ripped tissue paper glued on.

Designer: Rachel Bright. Photographic manipulation by John Russell and Emma Julings. With thanks to Emma Helborough and Non Figg.
This edition first published in 2011 by Usborne Publishing Ltd. Usborne House, 83-85 Saffron Hill, London EC1N 8RT, England. www.usborne.com